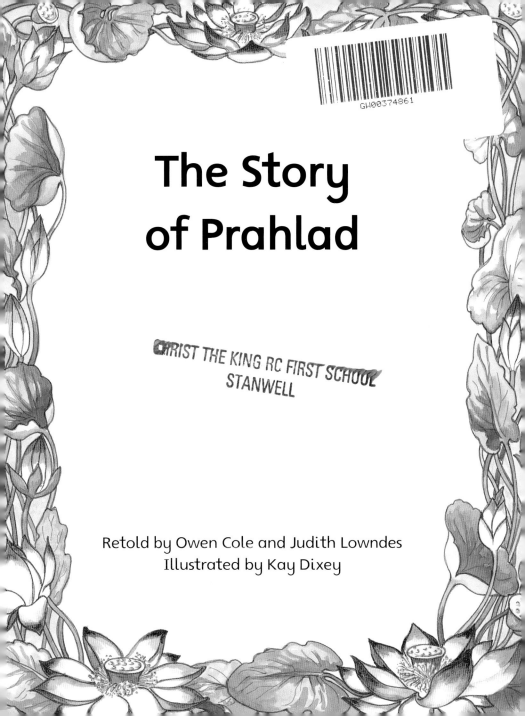

The Story of Prahlad

Retold by Owen Cole and Judith Lowndes
Illustrated by Kay Dixey

Heinemann Educational Publishers
Halley Court, Jordan Hill, Oxford OX2 8EJ

MADRID   ATHENS   PARIS
FLORENCE   PRAGUE   WARSAW
PORTSMOUTH NH   CHICAGO   SAO PAULO
SINGAPORE   TOKYO   MELBOURNE   AUCKLAND
IBADAN   GABORONE   JOHANNESBURG

© Heinemann Educational 1995

First published 1995

95 96 97 98 99 10 9 8 7 6 5 4 3 2 1

British Library Cataloguing in Publication Data
A catalogue record for this book is available from the British Library

Starter Pack
1 of each of 12 titles: ISBN 0 435 01066 2

Library Hardback Edition
The Story of Prahlad: ISBN 0 431 07756 8
1 of each of 12 titles: ISBN 0 431 07763 0

Designed by Sue Vaudin; printed and bound in Hong Kong

Acknowledgements
Back cover photograph:
Ann & Bury Peerless

Holi is a special time of year for Hindus.
They play games, have parties and tell special stories.

This is one of the stories that Hindus
tell at Holi time.
It helps them remember how good
God is.

This story has been told for
thousands of years.
It is about a God called Vishnu.

There was once a wicked king who
said that he was a God.
He said that people had to worship him.

This bad king had a son called Prahlad.

Prahlad was a good boy.

He knew that his father was not a God.

Prahlad felt that Vishnu was a true God.
Prahlad wanted to worship Vishnu.

This made the wicked king really angry.

"You must worship me!" he shouted.

But Prahlad said, "No.
You are not a God.
Vishnu is a true God.
I want to worship Vishnu."

The king was so angry that he made
some evil plans to punish poor Prahlad.

The wicked king told his soldiers to
get an elephant.
He said they must make the elephant
charge at Prahlad and trample him.

Prahlad heard the thunder of
the elephant's feet.
He saw it charging him.
"Help me Lord Vishnu," he cried.
"Save me!"

When the elephant saw Prahlad it
bowed down in front of him.
Prahlad was safe.

"Dig a deep pit!" the bad king said to
his soldiers.

"Fill it with deadly snakes and throw
Prahlad in."

So poor Prahlad was thrown into
the snake pit.

Prahlad prayed to Vishnu.

"Help me Lord Vishnu," he cried.

"Save me!"

Not one snake bit Prahlad.

He was safe.

Now, the wicked king was very angry.
"You must worship me, Prahlad!" he
shouted.
But Prahlad still said, "No.
I worship Vishnu."

Prahlad had a wicked sister called Holika.

She had magic powers.

Holika said to the king, "I will
punish Prahlad for you."

"Good!" said the king.

She made a huge bonfire and lit it.
"Come with me into the fire," she
said to Prahlad.
"My magic will save us."

Holika wanted Prahlad to burn in
the flames.

She was very wicked.

Prahlad and Holika walked into the fire.

"Help me Lord Vishnu," cried Prahlad as they went into the flames.
"Save me!"

Again, Lord Vishnu saved Prahlad.
Prahlad walked safely out of the fire.
It was the wicked Holika who died.
Vishnu had shown that he
cared for Prahlad.